Introduction by Jerry Garcia
Edited by Jeff Tamarkin and David Schreiner

HYPERION

New York

Library of Congress Cataloging-in-Publication Data

Grateful Dead comix (Comic strip)
Grateful Dead comix / introduction by Jerry Garcia : edited by Jeff Tamarkin and
David Schreiner.—1st ed.
p.   cm.
''Grateful Dead comix are adapted from the comic book series originated by Kitchen
Sink Press''—
Sixteen Grateful Dead classic songs interpreted by leading comic book artists.
ISBN 1-56282-971-8
1. Grateful Dead (Musical Group)—Comic books, strips, etc. I. Tamarkin, Jeff.
II. Schreiner, David. III. Grateful Dead (Musical Group) IV. Title. V. Title: Grateful Dead
comix.
PN6727.G74G73 1992
741.5'973—dc20                                                                                    92-9139
                                                                                                            CIP

Slipcased limited edition hardcover of this collection published by Kitchen Sink Press,
Inc., of Princeton WI. ISBN 0-87816-169-4.

*Grateful Dead Comix* are adapted from the comic book series
originated by Kitchen Sink Press.

First Edition

10  9  8  7  6  5  4  3  2  1

# Contents

# Introduction

*By Jerry Garcia*

I've always thought the comics were just a great way to tell a story, you know—pictures and words and good ideas. *Grateful Dead Comix* has been fun and satisfying, although in some sense I tend to think of it as a tribute to the EC comics we all grew up on.

The first comic that made an impression on me was an EC that my stepfather gave me when I was eight or nine. It was beat up, it didn't have a cover on it, it was absolutely hideous, really horrible—just perfect. I had asthma as a kid so I got into reading and the way I got into reading was from these comics. I got fascinated by them, by the horribleness of them, for one thing, and by the tongue-in-cheek humor. I found them funny and reasonable and wise, in a kind of Old Testament way—of course, I didn't know it in those words at that time—but EC comics were always eye for an eye, the bad guy always got it. They were horrible, but they were really well executed, the drawings were excellent and so forth, in fact unparalleled to this day—Wally Wood, Jack Davis, Bill Elder, Harvey Kurtzmann, they even had Frank Frizetta for a little while. *Tales from the Crypt, Vault of Horror, Haunt of Fear, Shock Suspense Stories*—I just loved them, and I started collecting them.

Later on in the fifties the comic-regulation deal clamped down heavy on EC. Now, the other thing about EC comic books was that they had a fantastic readership—the readers were very active; the letters-to-the-editor page was always hilarious; there was this continual row going on between the editors and the readers—called "fanaddicts" (fanatics)—and when the government started persecuting the editors, the readers stuck up tremendously for them—"I'm a schoolteacher and I love these comics . . . blah blah." It was kind of a heroic effort by a small group of people who loved what they were doing, not unlike the Grateful Dead. The parallels are fairly obvious—they were dealing with it in the graphic world, but they had their following, like Dead Heads, and they were very devoted to their following, too, they addressed them directly, and they took into account what they said, and so forth. The whole thing had that populist hero kind of quality to it—the struggling little publishing company taking on the government. . . .

Anyway, they finally hit it big with *Mad* comics, which turned into *Mad* magazine, and Bill Gaines is still at it. Most of those guys graduated, some of them went on to tragic ends, and they've been a running sidebar to my life. And then, of course, when I became a freak, I started to meet all the younger cartoonists who'd been influenced by EC like I was, and they started to put out the underground comics which in a way owed a lot to EC comics except they were like "Okay, now let's put out comics the way we want them with absolutely nobody telling us what to do, *completely* wide open, you can have anything in them." And that was my second phase of comics—I was a collector then too, *Zap,* and so forth.

So *Grateful Dead Comix* has been the realization of some very old dreams. Our models are the best quality things that are coming out, so we're trying to hang in that top category, in terms of production values, although the artists are on their own—I wouldn't want to be telling anybody what to write. But presumably they're finding something of value in the songs, and some of them are really powerful stuff, especially "Dire Wolf" and "Cumberland Blues." That's like having something realized in a really nice way—it scratches the itch. The covers are tremendous, too. The Grateful Dead has always been eclectic stylistically, and so are these comics, going from hard illustrative styles to cartoony, comic-y, bouncy animated stuff. Being able to have that spread of style is fun. I don't know that there's any absolute aesthetic to comics, just like music, and whether or not this material has any interest to anybody besides Dead Heads I couldn't even begin to guess. It doesn't matter, really.

For me, it's given me new covers to collect, and made me a happy fan. Still a fanaddict after all these years.

Jerry Garcia
*San Rafael, 1991*

# DIRE WOLF

TIMOTHY TRUMAN: 1991

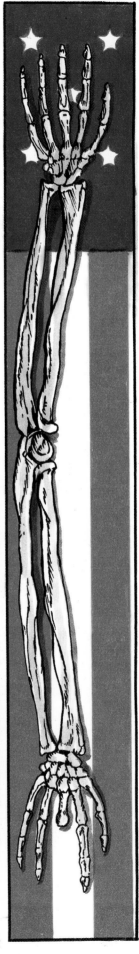

3

WHEN I AWOKE THE DIRE WOLF... SIX HUNDRED POUNDS OF SIN...
WAS GRINNING AT MY WINDOW... ALL I SAID WAS "COME ON IN..."

DON'T MURDER ME... I BEG OF YOU, DON'T MURDER ME... PLEASE...
DON'T MURDER ME...

HE WOLF CAME IN, I GOT MY CARDS...
                    WE SAT DOWN FOR A GAME...

CUT MY DECK TO THE QUEEN OF SPADES...

...BUT THE CARDS WERE ALL THE SAME...

6

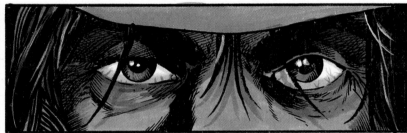

O N THE BACKWASH OF FENNARIO
THE BLACK AND MUDDY MIRE
THE DIRE WOLF COLLECTS HIS DUE
WHILE THE BOYS SING 'ROUND THE FIRE...

DON'T MURDER ME...
I BEG OF YOU, DON'T MURDER ME...
PLEASE ...
DON'T MURDER ME...
I BEG OF YOU,
PLEASE...
DON'T MURDER ME .

Drivin' that train, High on Cocaine...
CASEY JONES
TOOT!
...you better watch your speed

FRIEND OF THE DVIL

...THE GRATEFUL DEAD : CANCIÓN

18

I SET OUT RUNNING BUT I TAKE MY TIME, A FRIEND OF THE DEVIL IS A FRIEND OF MINE. IF I GET HOME BEFORE DAYLIGHT, JUST MIGHT GET SOME SLEEP TONIGHT.

el escorpion

I RAN DOWN TO THE LEVEE BUT THE DEVIL CAUGHT ME THERE. HE TOOK MY TWENTY-DOLLARS AND HE VANISHED IN THE AIR.

el buho

DIABLO

...mas amigos del diablo.

YOU CAN BORROW FROM THE DEVIL, YOU CAN BORROW FROM A FRIEND, BUT THE DEVIL'LL GIVE YOU TWENTY WHEN YOUR FRIEND GOT ONLY TEN.

VINO

SET OUT RUNNING BUT I TAKE MY TIME...

...A FRIEND OF THE DEVIL IS A FRIEND OF MINE.

el lagarto

el león

25

BUT, AS THE MUSIC SWIRLED, AND THE FIRST STARS APPEARED, ALL CARES VANISHED. ABOVE ME, THE TOWERING ROCKS THEMSELVES SEEMED TO DANCE TO THE THUDDING BASS, WHILE BELOW, THE LIGHTS OF DENVER SPREAD LIKE A NEW SKY AT MY FEET...

29

30

# Cumberland Blues

TIMOTHY TRUMAN

CAN'T STAY MUCH LONGER, MELINDA. THE SUN IS GETTING HIGH...

CAN'T HELP YOU WITH YOUR TROUBLES IF YOU WON'T HELP WITH MINE.

**I** GOTTA GET DOWN... **I** GOTTA GET DOWN... **G**OT TO GET DOWN TO THE MINE...

**Y**OU KEEP ME UP JUST ONE MORE NIGHT-- I CAN'T SLEEP HERE NO MORE...

**L**ITTLE BEN CLOCK SAYS QUARTER TO EIGHT... YOU KEPT ME UP TILL FOUR...

**I** GOTTA GET DOWN... I GOTTA GET DOWN... OR I CAN'T WORK THERE NO MORE.

GOTTA POOR MAN MAKE A FIVE-DOLLAR BILL...

...KEEP HIM HAPPY ALL THE TIME...

33

"CAN I GO, BUDDY? CAN I GO DOWN-- TAKE YOUR SHIFT AT THE MINE?"...

GOT TO GET DOWN TO THE CUMBERLAND MINE. THAT'S WHERE I MAINLY SPEND MY TIME..

MAKE GOOD MONEY-- FIVE DOLLARS A DAY. MAKE ANY MORE I MIGHT MOVE AWAY.

LOTTA POOR MAN GOT THE CUMBERLAND BLUES...

...HE CAN'T WIN FOR LOOSIN'...

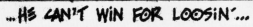

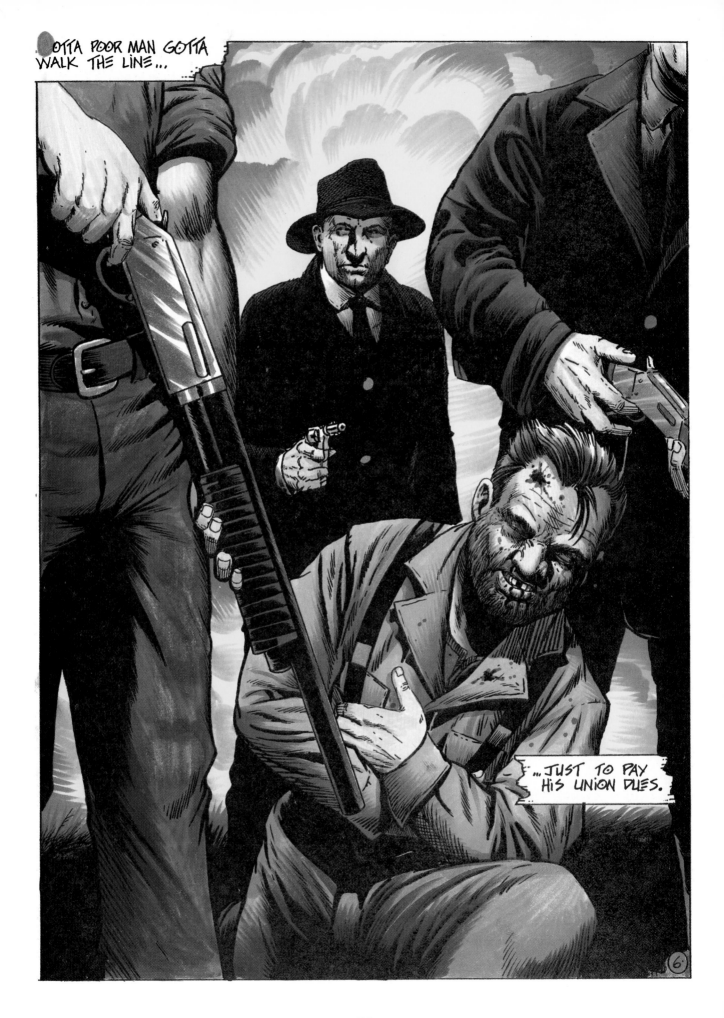

I DON'T KNOW NOW-- I JUST DON'T KNOW-- IF I'M GOIN' BACK AGAIN...

I DON'T KNOW NOW-- I JUST DON'T KNOW...

...IF I'M GOIN' BACK AGAIN.

· THE END ·

COLD IRON SHACKLES
and a BALL and CHAIN

LISTEN to the WHISTLE
of the EVENING TRAIN

YOU KNOW YOU BOUND
to WIND UP DEAD

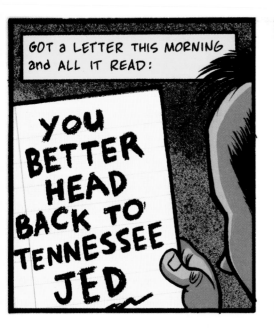

GOT a LETTER THIS MORNING and ALL IT READ:

YOU BETTER HEAD BACK TO TENNESSEE JED

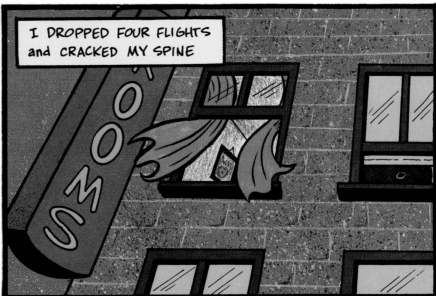

I DROPPED FOUR FLIGHTS and CRACKED MY SPINE

HONEY, COME QUICK WITH the IODINE

CATCH a FEW WINKS DOWN UNDER the BED THEN HEAD BACK to TENNESSEE, JED

TENNESSEE, TENNESSEE; THERE AIN'T NO PLACE I'D RATHER BE; BABY WON'T YOU CARRY ME BACK to TENNESSEE

I WOKE UP a-FEELING MEAN

WENT DOWN to PLAY the SLOT MACHINE

THE WHEELS TURNED ROUND and the LETTERS READ:

BETTER HEAD

BACK TO

TENN-ESSEE, JED

# TALES FROM TERRAPIN STATION

**TERRAPIN STATION**
in the shadow of the moon
Terrapin Station
and I know we'll be there soon

**LADY WITH A FAN**
GARCIA & HUNTER
Art By
DAN STEFFAN

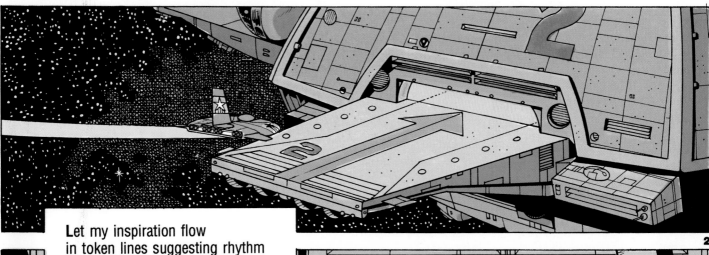

Let my inspiration flow
in token lines suggesting rhythm
that will not forsake me
till my tale is told and done

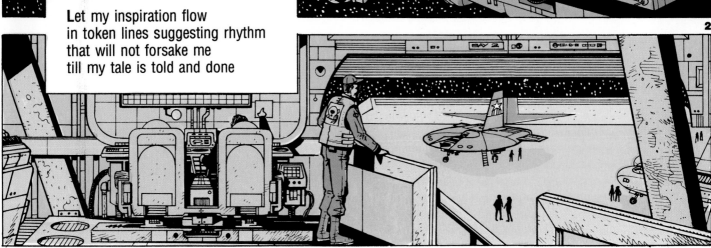

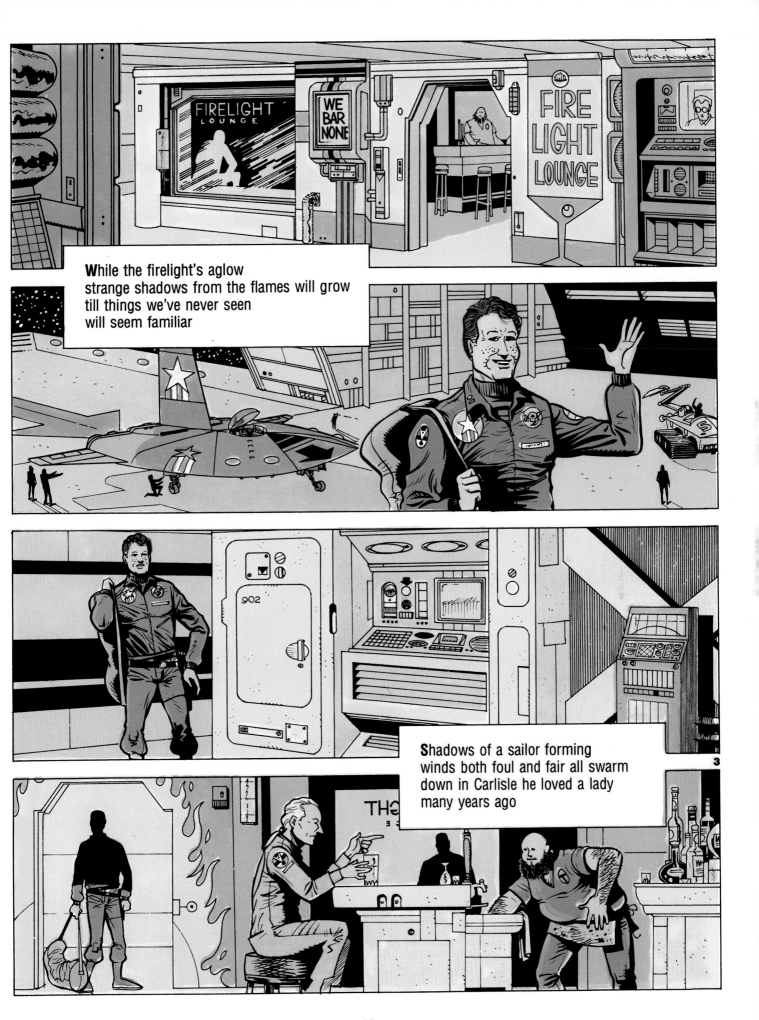

While the firelight's aglow
strange shadows from the flames will grow
till things we've never seen
will seem familiar

Shadows of a sailor forming
winds both foul and fair all swarm
down in Carlisle he loved a lady
many years ago

49

Here beside him stands a man
a soldier from the looks of him
who came through many fights
but lost at love

4

While the storyteller speaks
a door within the fire creaks
suddenly flies open
and a girl is standing there

Eyes alight with glowing hair
all that fancy paints as fair
she takes her fan and throws it
in the lion's den

5

"**W**hich of you to gain me, tell
will risk the uncertain pains of Hell?
I will not forgive you
if you will not take the chance."

6

The sailor gave at least a try
the soldier being much too wise
strategy was his strength
and not disaster

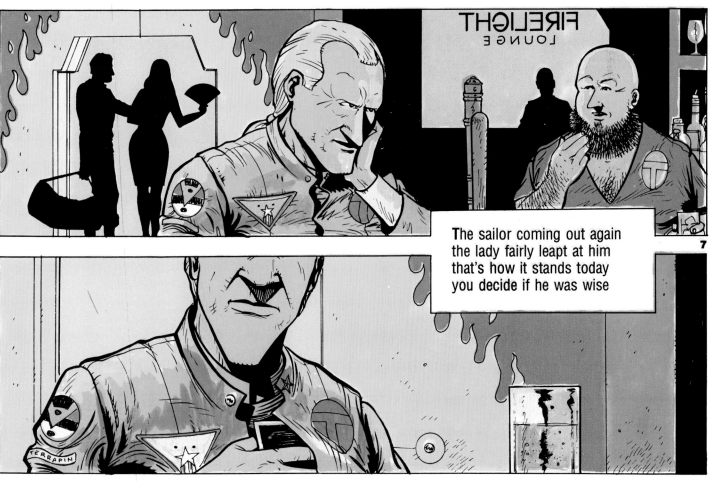

The sailor coming out again
the lady fairly leapt at him
that's how it stands today
you decide if he was wise

7

The storyteller makes no choice
soon you will not hear his voice
his job is to shed light
and not to master

Since the end is never told
we pay the teller off in gold
in hopes he will come back
but he cannot be bought or sold

8

end

# Terrapin Station

By GARCIA & HUNTER

Art By DAN STEFFAN

Inspiration move me brightly
light the song with sense and color,
hold away despair

2

56

More than this I will not ask
faced with mysteries dark and vast
statements just seem vain at last
some rise, some fall, some climb
to get to Terrapin

3

57

Counting stars by candlelight
all are dim but one is bright:
the spiral light of Venus
rising first and shining best,

From the northwest corner
of a brand-new crescent moon
crickets and cicadas sing
a rare and different tune

4

58

5

Terrapin Station
in the shadow of the moon
Terrapin Station
and I know we'll be there soon

6

Terrapin—I can't figure out
Terrapin—if it's an end or the beginning
Terrapin—but the train's got its brakes on
and the whistle is screaming: *Terrapin*

7

61

While you were gone
these spaces filled with darkness

The obvious was hidden
With nothing to believe in
the compass always points to Terrapin

The sullen wings of fortune beat like rain
You're back in Terrapin for good or ill again
For good or ill again

ARROWS OF NEON AND FLASHING MARQUEES OUT ON MAIN STREET

CHICAGO, NEW YORK, DETROIT IT'S ALL ON THE SAME STREET

A TYPICAL CITY INVOLVED IN A TYPICAL DAYDREAM

HANG IT UP AND SEE WHAT TOMORROW BRINGS

DALLAS—GOT A SOFT MACHINE

HOUSTON—TOO CLOSE TO NEW ORLEANS

NEW YORK—GOT THE WAYS AND MEANS BUT JUST WON'T LET YOU BE

MOST OF THE CATS YOU MEET ON THE STREET SPEAK OF TRUE LOVE

MOST OF THE TIME THEY'RE SITTIN' AND CRYIN' AT HOME

ONE OF THESE DAYS THEY KNOW THEY GOTTA GET GOIN'

OUT OF THE DOOR AND DOWN TO THE STREET ALL ALONE

TRUCKIN~LIKE THE DOODAH MAN
ONCE TOLD ME YOU GOT TO PLAY YOUR HAND
SOMETIME~THE CARDS AIN'T WORTH A DIME
IF YOU DON'T LAY 'EM DOWN

BUSTED—
   DOWN ON BOURBON STREET
SET UP—
   LIKE A BOWLING PIN
KNOCKED DOWN—
   IT GETS TO WEARING THIN
THEY JUST WON'T
   LET YOU BE

YOU'RE SICK OF HANGING AROUND AND YOU'D LIKE TO TRAVEL

TIRED OF TRAVEL, YOU WANT TO SETTLE DOWN

I GUESS THEY CAN'T REVOKE YOUR SOUL FOR TRYIN'...

SOMETIMES THE LIGHT'S ALL SHINING ON ME

OTHER TIMES I CAN BARELY SEE

LATELY IT OCCURS TO ME—WHAT A LONG STRANGE TRIP IT'S BEEN

TRUCKIN'—
    I'M GOIN' HOME
WHOA-OH, BABY, BACK WHERE I BELONG
BACK HOME—SIT DOWN AND PATCH MY BONES

        AND GET BACK TRUCKIN' ON

THE END

72

MEANWHILE, THE BAND WAS ALREADY BACKSTAGE, IN LILLE, WAITING FOR THE EQUIPMENT TRUCK TO ARRIVE...

NE PAS FUMER

PSSST! PHIL!

C'M'RE. QUICK. BUMMER NEWS.

WHAT?

C'M'RE, DAMMIT!

LA LOGE

IT'S THE *EQUIPMENT TRUCK*, MAN. DEAD IN TH' WATER. IT'S NOT GONNA *MAKE* IT.

THE *EQUIPMENT TRUCK*?

?

GET THE BUS. BACK IT UP TO THE WINDOW. QUICK.

IT'S THERE.

WE...MAY HAVE A LITTLE PROBLEM.

THE TRUCK WITH ALL OUR STUFF IN IT. IT'S.... UH...*MORTE*.

4

74

WRITTEN BY:

ART BY:

JERRY GARCIA,
BILL KREUTZMANN, PHIL LESH,
RON McKERNAN AND BOB WEIR

DAN BURR

SEE THAT GIRL

BAREFOOTIN' ALONG

WHISTLIN' AND SINGIN',

SHE'S A-CARRYIN' ON

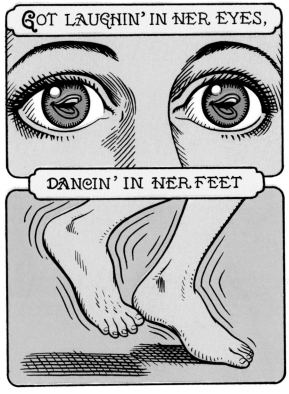

GOT LAUGHIN' IN HER EYES,

DANCIN' IN HER FEET

SHE'S A NEON LIGHT DIAMOND,

SHE CAN LIVE ON THE STREET

Ney, ney, come right away

Come and join the party, ev'ry day

Ney, ney, come right away

Come and join the party ev'ry day

80

TAKE A VACATION, FALL OUT FOR A WHILE

SUMMER'S COMIN' IN AND IT'S GOIN' OUT-A-STYLE

WELL, LIE DOWN SMOKIN', HONEY, HAVE YOURSELF A BALL

'CAUSE YOUR MOTHER'S DOWN IN MEMPHIS,

WON'T BE BACK TILL THE FALL

Adapted by Timothy Truman from the song by Robert Hunter & Jerry Garcia. Special thanks to Roger Petersen.

JST ONE THING I ASK OF YOU... JUST ONE THING FOR ME...

PEASE FORGET YOU KNEW MY NAME...

MY DARLING SUGAREE.

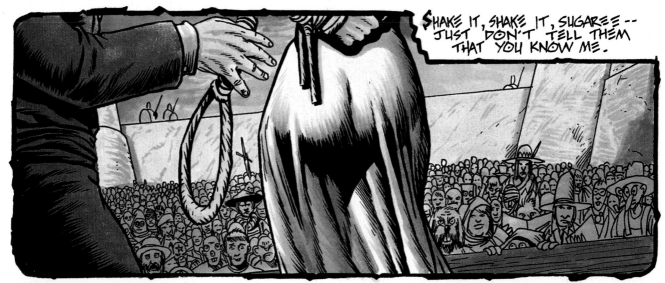

SHAKE IT, SHAKE IT, SUGAREE -- JUST DON'T TELL THEM THAT YOU KNOW ME.

YOU THOUGHT YOU WAS THE COOL FOOL-- NEVER COULD DO NO WRONG ...

MURDERESS CONFESSES "I WORKED ALONE"

... HAD EVERYTHING SEWED UP TIGHT. HOW COME YOU LAY AWAKE ALL NIGHT LONG ?

JUST ONE THING I ASK OF YOU... JUST ONE THING FOR ME... PLEASE FORGET YOU KNEW MY NAME MY DARLING SUGAREE.

86

Shake it, shake it, sugaree. Just don't tell them that you know me...
You know in spite of all you've gained you still have to stand out in the pouring rain..

...One last voice is calling you...

...And I guess it's time to go.

JUST ONE THING I ASK OF YOU... JUST ONE THING FOR ME.

PLEASE FORGET THAT YOU KNEW MY NAME...

... MY DARLING, SUGAREE.

JUST ONE THING I ASK OF YOU... JUST ONE THING FOR ME.

SHAKE IT, SHAKE IT, SUGAREE... JUST DON'T TELL THEM THAT YOU KNOW ME...

SHAKE IT UP NOW, SUGAREE.
I'LL MEET YOU AT THE
        JUBILEE.
AND IF THAT JUBILEE DON'T
        COME
MAYBE I'LL MEET YOU ON THE RUN.

ONE THING I ASK OF YOU...
JUST ONE THING FOR ME...
PLEASE FORGET YOU KNEW MY NAME...
MY DARLING SUGAREE!

SHAKE IT, SHAKE IT, SUGAREE. BUT DON'T TELL THEM THAT YOU KNOW ME...

SHAKE IT, SHAKE IT, SUGAREE. JST DON'T TELL'EM THAT YOU KNOW ME...

 THE·END

BEEN HERE SO LONG

HE'S GOT TO CALLING IT HOME

FORTUNE COME ACRAWLING

CALLIOPE WOMAN

SPINNING SENSE THAT CURIOUS SENSE OF YOUR OWN...

CAN YOU ANSWER?

YES, I CAN

BUT WHAT WOULD BE THE ANSWER TO THE ANSWER MAN?

END

KEEP A-ROLLING-- JUST A MILE TO GO...

KEEP A-ROLLING, MY OLD BUDDY. YOU'RE MOVING MUCH TOO SLOW.

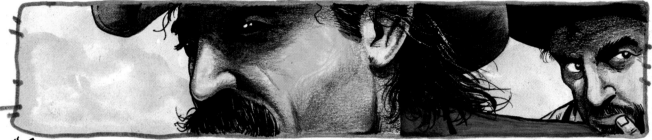

"I JUST JUMPED THE WATCHMAN RIGHT OUTSIDE THE FENCE. TOOK HIS RING, FOUR BUCKS IN CHANGE-- NOW AIN'T THAT HEAVEN SENT?"

HURTS MY EARS TO LISTEN, SHANNON. BURNS MY EYES TO SEE...

CUT DOWN A MAN IN COLD BLOOD, SHANNON...

...MIGHT AS WELL BE ME.

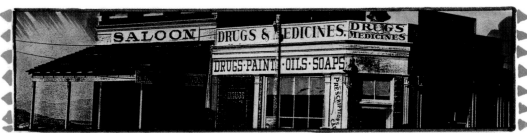

We USED TO PLAY FOR SILVER.. Now WE PLAY FOR LIFE. One'S FOR SPORT AND ONE'S FOR BLOOD...

...AT THE POINT OF A KNIFE.

Now THE DIE IS SHAKEN...
Now THE DIE MUST FALL...

THERE AIN'T A WINNER IN THIS GAME Who DON'T GO HOME WITH ALL ...

...NOT WITH ALL ...

LEAVING TEXAS, FOURTH DAY OF JULY. SUN SO HOT, CLOUDS SO LOW, EAGLES FILLED THE SKY.

CATCH THE DETROIT LIGHTNING OUT OF SANTA FE...

GREAT NORTHERN OUT OF CHEYENNE FROM SEA TO SHINING SEA.

GOTTA GET TO TULSA FIRST TRAIN WE CAN RIDE...

"GOT TO SETTLE ONE OLD SCORE... ONE SMALL POINT OF PRIDE."

AIN'T NO PLACE A MAN CAN HIDE, SHANNON,
KEEP HIM FROM THE SUN.

AIN'T NO BED WILL GIVE US REST, MAN...

...YOU KEEP US ON THE RUN.

JACK STRAW FROM WICHITA
CUT HIS BUDDY DOWN.
DUG FOR HIM A SHALLOW GRAVE
AND LAID HIS BODY DOWN.

HALF A MILE FROM TUCSON
BY THE MORNING LIGHT...

7.

She said her name was Billy Jean and she was fresh in town...

I didn't know a stageline ran from hell...

She had raven hair,

YOU ARE HERE

a ruffled dress,

a necklace made of gold

and all the French perfume you'd care to smell.

117

Then a man rode into town... some thought he was the law.

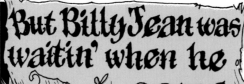

But Billy Jean was waitin' when he came...

She told me he would take her if I didn't use my gun

and I'd have no one but myself to blame

I went down to those dusty streets... Blood was on my mind...

I guess that stranger hadn't heard the news 'Cause I shot first and killed him, Lord, he didn't even draw...